Praise for **FINDING JOY IN MEDICINE**

"In *Finding Joy in Medicine* Reza Manesh has crafted a magnificent love song to medicine. Part memoir, part reflection, this short work echoes with the beauty and suspense, the exhilaration and heartbreaks of love itself. And throughout it all, like a bass line, flows the essential wonder and pleasures of learning and teaching. A joy to read."

—Lisa Sanders, MD, Yale School of Medicine, Contributing Writer, *New York Times Magazine*

"The journey from layperson to physician is, in essence, a typical professional transformation of novice to expert. But in this soulful memoir, Reza Manesh makes clear that the journey is about far more than the acquisition of technical expertise. It's about calibrating confidence and humility, about knowing when less is more, about connecting with the right role models and mentors, and about finding sources of satisfaction and joy in the face of frequent tragedy. While the phenomenon of physician burnout is very real, reading *Finding Joy in Medicine* reminded me of the unique privilege of being a doctor."

—Dr. Robert M. Wachter, Professor and Chair, Dept. of Medicine, University of California, San Francisco, author of *The Digital Doctor: Hope, Hype and Harm at the Dawn of Medicine's Computer Age*

"In *Finding Joy in Medicine*, Reza shares his journey to becoming a renowned physician, beloved teacher, and inspiring mentor to countless students around the world. Filled with moving reflections and pearls of wisdom from Reza and those he has learned from, this book is a master class in humility and humanity. *Finding Joy in Medicine* should be required reading for everyone practicing or studying medicine."

—Dr. Aaron Berkowitz, author of *One by One by One: Making a Small Difference Amid a Billion Problems*

"A career in medicine is an intense journey filled with emotional juxtapositions. There is tremendous achievement and deep sadness; joy and guilt, boundless elation and crushing fatigue. In *Finding Joy in Medicine*, Dr. Manesh's glorious ode to this incredible profession, we see and feel his odyssey which in turn helps us come to grips with our own journey. This is a wonderful gift from a remarkable teacher, Dr. Manesh's book will resonate deeply."

—Mark Shapiro, MD, Creator and Host, Explore The Space Podcast

"Through humility and humanity, authenticity and vulnerability, Dr. Manesh shares the origin and evolution of his passion for being a consummate and caring clinician and teacher. The insights Reza shares about how he learned to say "I don't know"—and his ongoing work in the medical community to champion safe spaces to be able to say that at all ages and stages of practice—stand to dramatically reshape how medicine embraces growth mindset. His sage wisdom is raw, deeply moving, and gorgeously shared. This book deserves to be required reading, and it is one for the ages."

—Avital O'Glasser, MD, FACP, FHM, Associate Professor of Medicine, Oregon Health & Science University School of Medicine

"In this book, Reza Manesh recounts experiences so many of us in medicine have shared—waywardness, uncertainty, even depression. Yet he finds himself in a position of strength, and he uses that strength to support others, following in the footsteps of his own beloved Aghajoon. His message is that it is not only possible to be both a fallible human and an excellent physician, but further that it is only through acknowledging and learning from our fallibility that we can become excellent. I think readers will find comfort and a challenge in this book, and I highly recommend it."

—Elisabeth Askin, MD, author of *The Health Care Handbook: A Clear and Concise Guide to the United States Health Care System*

"Clinician-educators are often unknown outside their institutions, but in their institutions they are revered role models. Reza writes passionately about his role models (starting with his grandfather) and how they have shaped him. He talks about the secret sauce for clinician-educator success—passion. The "greats" love medicine and helping their learners grow. They work hard to improve and their learners benefit. Reza's journey provides readers with an understanding of that passion, with the never-ending help of his beloved Aghajoon."

—Robert M. Centor, MD, Professor of Medicine, University of Alabama School of Medicine

FINDING
JOY
in Medicine

REZA MANESH, MD

Foreword by Kimberly Manning, MD

Copyright © 2021 by Reza Manesh
rezamanesh.com
All rights reserved.

Published in the United States by Aghajoon LLC.

ISBN 978-1-7370983-0-0 Paperback
ISBN 978-1-7370983-1-7 Ebook
ISBN 978-1-7370983-2-4 Audiobook

Cover design: robinlockemonda.com
Interior design: asyablue.com

For Aghajoon

عشق است که امید دهد هستی ما را

برعالم هستی بدهد صلح وصفارا

عشق بود پایه و بنیاد دو عالم

ورنه نتوان طی نمود دار فنارا

هر کس به امیدی ره خودپیش گرفته

تسهیل کند بر خودش اعمال بقا را

دنیا همه عشق است بهر جا که نهی پای

باید بخودت رنج دهی زحمت پارا

بی عشق چو زندان بود این عالم هستی

با عشق توان کرد زخود دور جفارا

جز عشق نباشد که بر این درد علاجی

با عشق توان کرد بر این درد، دوارا

Passion is the foundation of life

It gives peace and serenity to our existence

Passion and love are the pillars of this universe and beyond

Without love and passion life is meaningless

Each person lives their life in search of a purpose

Purpose allows protection from the challenges of life

You will find love and passion wherever you step

But you must take the first step

Without love the universe is like a prison

With love you can deflect grief

Without love and passion there is no remedy for misery

Love and passion are the treatment to such misery

— Abbas Amiraslani, aka, Aghajoon

CONTENTS

FINDING
JOY
in Medicine

FOREWORD

"Does your face light up?"

These were the words of the late author and Nobel laureate Toni Morrison. She was speaking of the power of putting our love on display for those who matter most in our lives. "That's what they're looking for," she said. No truer words have ever been spoken.

While scrolling through social media one day, I came across this image Reza posted on his thread. I enlarged the image for a better look. A man with greying hair gazed upward from a sundrenched porch into the camera. Warmth poured from his open expression. His mouth was slightly parted as if preparing to speak loving words of affirmation to whomever had taken the photo. And then there were his eyes—brownish-amber and dancing with light and affection. I would learn that this man was Reza's grandfather—or Aghajoon as he affectionately called him. Quickly, I typed a comment beneath the post: "Did you take this photo, Reza?"

Mostly, it was a rhetorical question. Something told me that he was the one who'd pointed that lens in Aghajoon's direction that day. Turns out I was right.

Toni Morrison went on to explain that a loving, approving gaze is where a child first finds their value and belief in self. Just one look at Aghajoon in that faded photo explains much about Dr. Manesh and the passion he brings to medicine. His interactions with his patients, his peers, and the countless learners is an homage to the devotion that enveloped him from his earliest years. The love is on display. His face—and even his voice—lights up every single time.

Beyond children, what then does this mean? For patients, it translates to building therapeutic alliances and minimizing fear. For colleagues, it leads to a collaborative and celebratory vibe without competition. But especially, the light that twinkled in Aghajoon's face now explodes from Reza into all he teaches. It is this that gives them all unspoken permission to be imperfect and growing—and the psychological safety to be vulnerable and evolve together.

Though the title of the book is *Finding Joy in Medicine*, I suspect that Aghajoon would tell us that joy begins from within and ripples outward to those we love and the things that matter. Every chapter of this book is a ripple from Reza that we, the readers, should take as a charge to toss forward as pebbles. More ripples, more pebbles, more joy. May we all reach inside to connect with what matters most and then put it on display through faces alight with encouragement, curiosity, and a belief of all that we can do—together.

—Kimberly Manning, MD

INTRODUCTION

Alarmed by the sight of her blood-filled toilet bowl, Ms. Harris drove to the hospital. As I palpated her abdomen to try to determine the cause of her bleeding, I looked beyond her to focus on the sensations beneath my fingertips. The bright fluorescent lights of the emergency room glinted off her wristwatch, drawing my attention to its unique, gold, sword-shaped hands.

"Tell me about your marvelous watch," I asked.

"My father wanted me to have the watch after he died," she said, choking up. "I wear it when I'm sick so I can feel his presence watching over me." She paused and looked at my neck. "And where did you get this beautiful necklace?"

"It's from my Aghajoon," I said, relaxing my pressure on her abdomen and turning to look at her. "That's Farsi for grandfather. I wear it so I feel his presence watching over me."

The ring with the red stone that I wear every day around my neck holds great meaning for me. Aghajoon was my first teacher. We would spend endless hours sitting cross-legged on the floor in his living room, playing backgammon while we sipped boiling Persian tea and sucked on sugar cubes. He would analyze each of my moves, explain the alternatives, and kiss my cheek when I won a game (which was rare). He taught me that no one starts out competent in anything. We only cultivate skills through lifelong learning. I apply this wisdom every day in my work as a doctor and in life in general.

I smiled at Ms. Harris to reassure her that we would find the cause of her bleeding, and she would recover. I felt confident I would make the right diagnosis and select the best treatment because that's what I spent the last decade learning how to do.

But I wasn't always this confident. I didn't get into medical school the first time I applied. I nearly killed a patient during my intern year. As an attending physician, I faced imposter syndrome and felt inadequate in my clinical and teaching skills.

These types of difficult moments are not unique to me, and not unique to doctors. I know my dear colleagues in medicine—nurses, physician assistants, nurse practitioners, respiratory therapists, physical therapists, nutritionists, speech and language pathologists, pharmacists, and all others who care for patients—face similar difficulties. We wonder whether we are good enough, struggle with how to come to terms with mistakes we make, and wrestle with alleviating the suffering endured by our patients, all while trying to lessen our own emotional and physical exhaustion.

Despite this, I have found joy in the practice of medicine.

This book is about three traits I learned to cultivate in order to find joy in medicine: humanism, humility, and hunger for growth.

None of these were formally taught to me. The stories in this book trace how I have sought to develop them over the course of my career. These are stories about finding my purpose. Stories about developing my passion. Stories about the impact I was able to have by combining my purpose and passion to become a physician focused on patients, learners, and the art of diagnosis.

I did ultimately discover the cause of Ms. Harris's bleeding, and she made a full recovery.

"See," she said to me tapping her watch and smiling on her way out of the hospital. "My father was watching over me."

I smiled back at her and tapped the red stone on my necklace. "And my Aghajoon was guiding me."

PART I

Purpose

1

Thirteen is an unlucky number in Iran. An entire holiday is based on eliminating its bad luck. *Sizdah Bedar* falls on the thirteenth day of Farvardin, the first month of the spring season, and translates roughly to "getting rid of thirteen," marking the end of the New Year Holiday and an opportunity for Iranians to wish each other luck on an unlucky day.

Despite the raging Iran-Iraq war, Iranians still celebrated *Sizdah Bedar* in 1985. In honor of the festival, Shahnaz, a 26-year-old woman, attended an evening picnic outside of Tehran with her husband, Mahmoud, and their two-year-old son, Ali. But amid the dancing, singing, eating, and laughing, Shahnaz whispered to her husband that she had a stomach ache. Mahmoud told her it was probably from eating too much *ash reshteh*—a creamy soup of noodles, vegetables, and yogurt—and told her to enjoy the party.

Shahnaz tried to ignore the pain, but it worsened. Still, Mahmoud told her she would be fine.

"Mahmoud, if I die, don't remarry," she pleaded, gripping his sleeve. "If you dare remarry, give Ali to my sister, Shahla."

He saw the fear in her eyes, the beads of sweat on her brow, her hands grabbing her swollen belly, eight months pregnant with their second child. They drove to the hospital, keeping their headlights off per government regulations to avoid attracting the attention of fighter jets. Fortunately, the light of a full moon illuminated their path.

When they arrived at the hospital, it was dark there too. The electricity had been turned off to lower the chance of a military attack.

Guided by candlelight, the doctor delivered Shahnaz a healthy baby boy just after midnight. What brief joy she had was interrupted by air raid sirens and the sound of explosions nearby. She desperately wanted to sleep with her baby that night, but the doctors and nurses would not allow it because of a specific evacuation protocol established by the hospital. So she and the other new mothers prayed all night that their newborns–and they–would survive the bombings.

After a sleepless night, the sun rose, and the 13th day was over. Mahmoud, Shahnaz, Ali, and their new baby went home in the safety of daylight.

"Reza," my mother later explained to me. "You must have been born on the 14th because everyone wished me so much luck on that 13th day of Farvardin."

2

The war was challenging for my parents, and that night in the hospital was the final straw. They could not continue to raise their children in the shadow of war. Despite my Maman's (Farsi for mom) successful career as a school teacher and my Baba (Farsi for father) having just finished in the top of his class in civil engineering, they left everything behind and moved to Austin, Texas, where my father had been accepted into a PhD program in civil engineering. They knew nobody there. And they barely spoke English.

In Austin, the four of us slept on one full-sized mattress in our tiny apartment. While studying for his PhD, my father worked at Burger King forty hours per week to put food on the table for us both figuratively and literally: the Whopper became our family's favorite meal.

Maman helped us with our homework, cooked, cleaned, and delivered enough love for my brother and me to make up for the lack of nearby relatives or friends. Every day, we arrived home from school to the aroma of steaming rice peppered with saffron and topped with a boiling stew. To this day, these dishes remind me of my mother's love and devotion to me and my brother.

My family returned to Iran when I was 12 years old. Baba had accepted a job as a civil engineer at an airport in Seoul, South Korea. Most of our extended relatives lived in Tehran, and my parents thought it would be best to be surrounded by them while my father was in Seoul. Two years later, Baba finished his job in Seoul and our family returned to the United States—now to Pittsburgh—where I started 9th grade. But I had missed a few crucial years and the other kids had already formed their friend groups. They laughed at my baggy Nike shirts and tight Levi's jeans. I went by Ray instead of Reza to try to fit in but remained an outsider. I ate lunch sitting on a toilet in a bathroom stall because I feared the embarrassment of sitting alone in a large cafeteria.

To fit in with the other kids, I desperately wanted video games, Starter jackets, and Air Jordan shoes. Determined to have them, I got a part-time job on the weekends washing dishes and cleaning bathrooms at Taco Bell. Spending my weekdays at school and doing homework and my weekends cleaning toilets drained me, but at least I got free chalupas with all the fixings.

I did the job diligently because I needed the paycheck to afford a home video game system. When I finally bought it and brought it home, I was hooked. Between Taco Bell and video games, my schoolwork began to suffer.

One day my father returned from his long day of work as a civil engineer and found me glued to my video game controller.

"Reza, did you do your homework?"

"Baba leave me alone! I'm almost at the next level!" I pleaded with my eyes fixed on the television.

"Reza! These video games will not lead to any success!" he yelled and tore the power cord from the outlet. He picked up the video game console and wrapped it in the cord.

"You are not getting this back until you finish your homework! Do you understand me?!"

"Yes, Baba," I said sheepishly, avoiding his stern gaze.

In that moment, I silently cursed my father and dreamed of the day I would move out. But in retrospect, I wonder how my parents did it. They left their family, culture, and everything they knew for me and my older brother Ali.

I was not a good student and didn't want to go to college. The only motivators were getting out of my parents' home and being close to my brother, who was a neuroscience major at the University of Pittsburgh (called "Pitt" for short). Ali had many friends, was great at soccer, and was a brilliant student who had been accepted into multiple colleges. I wanted to be like him—except for the brilliant student part (though I had the upper hand in video games). I applied to Pitt but was waitlisted.

My parents were disappointed, and I was ashamed. My neglect for schoolwork was having the consequences they had warned me about. Determined to get off the waitlist, I snapped into shape. Fueled by chocolate chip cookies and milk, I studied for hours. I found that when I engaged, classes suddenly became interesting. I asked questions, completed extra-credit assignments, and got near-perfect grades in my senior year of high school.

I made it off the wait list at Pitt and decided to major in neuroscience like my brother.

3

"If you are a first-year student, Intro to Neuroscience is not for you," Dr. Stricker said softly but sternly. "I am going to imagine this is the only course you are taking this semester. In fact, it will be the most challenging course you experience during college."

As I looked down from the back row of the lecture hall at this man in his tweed blazer and his thick-rimmed glasses, his sternness reminded me of my father threatening to take away my video games. His intimidating statements left me confused. He had a longstanding reputation of being one of the best professors at Pitt. Why was he trying to scare us out of the lecture hall? I thought of making for the door like several students did. But Ali had told me he was a stellar professor and the extra work would be worth it. Though I had just barely made it into college, I decided to accept the challenge and take his class my freshman year.

Dr. Stricker didn't require us to purchase any textbooks and he conducted open notebook exams. He was the first teacher who challenged me to develop understanding and critical thinking. Memorization was insufficient to ace his exams. Instead, his students had to be able to apply what they had learned to solve challenging new problems.

Fascinated by Dr. Stricker's class, and drawing on the study skills I had begun to cultivate in my effort to get into Pitt off the waitlist, I spent hours in a library cubicle using different colored pencils to rewrite every one of his lectures in my notebook.

Inspired by Dr. Stricker, I began working in his research lab, where we studied how rats regulate their fluid balance through thirst and hormone secretion. I could not stop thinking about the projects he assigned me and relished in the process of scientific inquiry and discovery.

I was learning that my previous lackluster performance in high school was not a reflection of my ability, but rather my lack of interest. I had never imagined learning could be more exciting than videogames. I thought of the life lessons I learned from Aghajoon over games of backgammon. "Reza jan," he would address me, his eyes glowing with love and wisdom. "Never lose your hunger for growth in any task. And remember, in our short existence on this earth, we should always be improving in all aspects of life."

Between classes and lab work, college flew by. I set my sights on applying to graduate school to become a neuroscientist and college professor just like Dr. Stricker.

4

Having ignited my passion for learning and conducting scientific experiments, and awed by Dr. Stricker's impact through teaching, I proudly told my parents I wanted to become a neuroscientist and college professor. But Maman and Baba wanted me to go to medical school and become a doctor. In Iranian society, becoming a doctor is seen as the pinnacle of professional aspirations. Many Iranians hope their children will become doctors, as it fills them with tremendous pride and bragging rights.

Desperately seeking my parents' approval, and wanting to make up for disappointing them by my subpar performance in high school, I followed their advice. I didn't want to go to medical school, but felt I needed to listen to my parents who had sacrificed so much for me.

Dr. Stricker was surprised when I returned to campus and told him I had changed my plans and would be applying to medical school. A scientist through and through, he simply asked, "Have you tested the hypothesis of whether becoming a doctor is the right fit for you?"

To answer his question, I volunteered at the University of Pittsburgh Medical Center (UPMC). If medicine wasn't for me, I would learn quickly and be able to justify to my parents why I should pursue my passion for science and teaching college students instead. As a volunteer, my role was simply to spend time talking with patients as they passed the long hours between family visits, medical procedures, and interactions with the medical teams. And so, donning a bright red volunteer blazer, I entered the hospital for the first time to test the hypothesis of whether a career in medicine was for me.

"Mr. Komarov, may I enter your room?" I asked anxiously after knocking, slightly opening his door, and softly speaking toward the center of the room.

"I don't want any visitors," he responded in a thick accent.

"Mr. Komarov, my name is Reza. I volunteer for the hospital. May I enter your room?"

"Do I have a choice?" he said, sighing.

I slowly opened the door. The room was pitch black. The television was off, and the blinds were down.

"May I turn on your lights?" I asked tentatively.

"If you have to."

The lights revealed a frail man with a thick gray beard that elongated his round face. His sunken eyes stared ahead, not looking at me.

"Would it be OK if I pull up a chair and sit next to you?" I cautiously asked.

"Do what you want. I am dying from cancer, what do I care?" he somberly responded.

We sat in uncomfortable silence.

"Mr. Komarov, I hear you have an accent. May I ask where you are from?" Thinking of my parents' Persian accents and their hardship in moving to America, I continued. "My family immigrated from Iran when I was two years old. We had no family in the United States. It was difficult," I hesitantly told him, thinking he was going to kick me out of his room.

"I was born in Moscow," he began. "I moved to the United States with the hope of making enough money to help my family in Russia. I worked as a taxi driver in New York City for three decades. I have no friends here. My family have all died. I became sick last year. And now I am dying."

"Mr. Komarov, I cannot imagine what you are going through," I said with tears forming in my eyes. I didn't know how to respond to his frankness about his mortality but thought at least I could provide him some company. "Tell me about your life before you got sick. What do you like to do?" I asked.

We talked for an hour. I learned how he fell in love at the age of nineteen, but left Russia and his first love to find prosperity in America. He enjoyed playing and watching soccer. New York-style pizza had become his favorite dish. And then he lost 60 pounds in the last year and was diagnosed with end-stage colon cancer.

Before I turned off his lights and left, he looked directly into my eyes for the first time since I'd entered his room and said, "Thank you for spending time with me."

He did not smile when he said those words, but it felt deeply meaningful. He was a man dying of cancer without any loved ones to lean on. I was a volunteer who couldn't provide any medical treatment. But I learned that just by being present, I could offer him some small connection so he would not suffer in solitude.

That day, I found my purpose in life: to care for patients like Mr. Komarov.

I was convinced that medicine was the right path, and I had the grades and research experience to be a competitive applicant to medical school. But I stumbled near the finish line by not studying enough for the MCAT, the medical school equivalent of the SAT. I was both overconfident and under-prepared. And my low score led me to be rejected from every single medical school I applied to.

At first, I wanted to give up. I hadn't wanted to go to medical school in the first place—that had been my parents' idea. I could go with the original neuroscience PhD plan, no MCAT required.

I sought out advice from Aghajoon. "Reza jan, follow your passion," he implored me during a visit from Iran. "Do what will bring you joy. And that will also bring joy to the world."

I thought of that feeling I had when meeting Mr. Komarov and so many other patients as a volunteer and knew what I needed to do. I trained for the MCAT like a marathon: prep course, practice tests, and study sessions day and night.

I tried again and was accepted to stay at Pitt for medical school. At first, I was excited, but then I felt uneasy. I hadn't been accepted to medical school the first time. And just a year earlier, I hadn't even wanted to apply to medical school at all. Was I on the right path?

5

In my first week of medical school, my system was shocked by the rapidity and volume of information presented. We were taught all of human anatomy in fifteen days: every single bone, muscle, nerve, and organ. Then we were expected to learn the complex field of genetics in just seven days. The environment was the opposite of Dr. Stricker's classes, where problem-solving and critical thinking were emphasized. In med school, it was all about memorizing as much as possible, as fast as possible.

There was no time to use my colored pencils that had helped me successfully navigate college by re-copying all my notes. I went into survival mode. "Pass equals MD," an upper-class student told me, chuckling when I asked him how to succeed. But even passing was no small feat. I paced back and forth on the nights before our weekly exams trying to memorize enough facts to pass without wasting a moment on sleep.

I would later learn that renowned Canadian physician Dr. William Osler said, "To study the phenomena of disease without books is to sail an uncharted sea, while to study books without patients is not to go to sea at all." But in the first year of medical school it was only books. We were not at sea in the hospital with patients, but docked at a tedious harbor of biochemistry, genetics, pharmacology, and microbiology, and it was making me seasick with anxiety and stress. I would later come to love these subjects, but only when I understood how they related to patient care.

I was sure I had made a mistake pursuing medical school. I barely passed the exams. I didn't enjoy learning the material. And in one year, I had already accumulated $40,000 of debt.

There were nights during my first two years of medical school where I looked out my third-floor window into the darkness and cried. I wondered whether all the pain would end if I jumped out. I soon discovered I was not the only one struggling, and my classmates and I leaned on each other to reduce the emotional pain. Knowing we were not alone in our struggles lowered our sense of defeat.

Nearly a third of medical students suffer from depression and ten percent experience suicidal thoughts. Medical students are three times more likely to die by suicide than peers of the same age. Medical schools have begun to consider student wellness and support, but we have a long way to go to improve our culture and ensure that students get the help they need before it's too late.

I survived the rest of the first two years of medical school by hearing that things would get better when we escaped the classroom for the hospital wards and clinics in the third year. Though we felt constantly behind in our efforts to memorize random facts taught at a breakneck pace, my fellow students and I kept telling each other to "Just Pass It" (referring to our exams), inspired by Nike's "Just Do It" slogan.

Finally, I had the opportunity to interact with patients during my third year of medical school. I found myself staying late in the hospital to talk with them. I enjoyed listening to their stories and holding their hands when they needed emotional support. Forging relationships with my patients reminded me of Mr. Komarov and why I applied to medical school in the first place. I had finally set sail on the sea Osler had described. Each patient taught me so much, motivating me to read everything I could to understand their illness and how to treat them.

Dr. Elmer Holzinger served as my very first clinical teacher during my third year of medical school. 82 years old and always wearing a crisp bowtie, he looked like the portraits of doctors of yesteryear in our school library. He was a warm and caring teacher. I was amazed at how he could hear a patient's story, examine them, and then teach the meaning of every phrase of the patient's history and every finding on the physical examination as clues toward making a diagnosis to treat the patient's illness.

When my dad developed a stripe of blisters over his right eye so painful he couldn't sleep, I called Dr. Holzinger.

"I am so sorry to bother you on the weekend, Dr. Holzinger," I said. "My dad is sick. I don't know what's wrong with him. He has painful blisters over his right eye."

"Reza, bring him to my office."

"But Dr. Holzinger, it's Saturday."

"I'll see you there."

Dr. Holzinger later told me that he already knew from the phone call alone that my dad had shingles.

The blistering rash, its painful nature, and its distribution following a specific nerve root were all characteristic of shingles, he taught me. But he wanted to obtain a history and perform a physical exam before prescribing any medications. "Reza you always need to confirm a hypothesis by talking to the patient, examining them, and then making a plan for their care together."

I was impressed not only by his encyclopedic knowledge, but also by how he cared for my father with such kindness, attention, and compassion—even on a Saturday and despite Baba not being his patient.

I knew I wanted to become like Dr. Holzinger one day, so I decided to follow in his footsteps and pursue my residency training in internal medicine.

6

"**A** 54-year-old man developed lower back pain four days ago," a senior resident presented to Dr. Gurpreet Dhaliwal, expert clinician and educator, in front of a group of University of California San Francisco (UCSF) residents and visiting medical students who were interviewing for residency positions there. I was one of those interviewees sitting in the first row in a packed conference room observing this living legend. Dr. Dhaliwal may be the only doctor to have been compared to a Hollywood director. The *New York Times* article describing his diagnostic acumen and skill at solving medical mysteries proclaimed, "To observe him at work is like watching Steven Spielberg tackle a script."

"Most adults will experience lower back pain in their lifetime, and the majority get better without any treatment," Dr. Dhaliwal confidently taught the room of residents and students. He continued, "I know the final diagnosis will be rare as I am discussing a clinical unknown in front of you and our applicants. But if I am being honest, I would not be concerned yet and would anticipate that the patient would improve without any treatment."

In medical education sessions like this, a resident physician presents a patient's case one piece at a time to an expert educator to learn from their thought process approaching a clinical problem. The audience and discussant do not know any details of the case before it is presented. Only the resident presenter is aware of how the story ends.

"He has had fevers for the past four days and point tenderness of his lower spine," the resident continued. "He is otherwise healthy without any other issues. No trauma. He went to the dentist a few weeks ago."

"While lower back pain is common, fever is a red flag and raises concern for a sinister process," Dr. Dhaliwal elucidated. "Fever points to inflammation, which is usually caused by an infection, cancer, or an autoimmune process. Infection is the most common cause of fever. The point tenderness localizes the site of disease to the lower spine. So, we know where the problem is, and we know what it likely is. To confirm, we would need an MRI of the spine."

The resident continued, "An MRI was performed. It showed destruction within the L4 vertebra."

"This is most likely infection, but spinal tumors can also cause such destruction," Dr. Dhaliwal responded. "The patient had a dental procedure a week prior. Usually a dental procedure and back pain are not related. But given the destructive process and fever, I am most concerned for a spinal infection from an oral *Streptococcal* species that traveled from the mouth through the blood to the heart and then to the spine."

I got goosebumps. This was the critical reasoning of Dr. Stricker combined with the clinical wisdom of Dr. Holzinger in a performance as riveting as a World Cup soccer match. I knew Dr. Dhaliwal was the mentor for me, and UCSF the place for me. Thanks to the guidance and support of Dr. Holzinger, I worked hard to excel in my clinical years of medical school despite my rocky start in the classroom.

I was accepted to train at UCSF and was over the moon to begin this next stage of my education.

PART II

Passion

7

When Mr. Johns suddenly became unconscious in his hospital bed, I was part of a team that sprang into action to try to save his life. An intern pushed up and down on his chest to take over for his heart, a senior resident snaked a breathing tube down his throat to help him breathe, and I tried to draw blood so we could send labs to figure out what was happening. I was still pretty inexperienced, and I kept trying to find a good vein, but I couldn't. Despite our best efforts, Mr. Johns did not survive. He was only 26, but years of living with AIDS and hepatitis C had taken their unfortunate toll on his body. Dejected, I walked out of the room and threw my gloves in the trash can.

Then I noticed my fingertip was bleeding.

I must have stuck myself amidst the chaos. I started to feel lightheaded. I might have just infected myself with both HIV and hepatitis C. I went immediately to see an occupational health specialist who told me I needed to take HIV medications for one month to try to prevent contracting the infection but there was nothing to reduce the risk of contracting hepatitis C.

The next day, I flew home for a brief vacation. My parents thought I was just tired from being an intern. But it was the HIV medicines. I was wracked with nausea and stomach pain and spent almost the whole visit in bed.

Though I had looked forward to spending time with my parents, it was a miserable week. I had nightmares and woke up in cold sweats, thinking I had either killed a patient, injured myself, or disappointed my parents by quitting medicine. In one of my nightmares, a patient's brain fell out of their skull because I had made a mistake. I picked it up from the ground, repositioned it, and put the skull back on like it was the lid of a container.

I spent my days feeling angry. Angry at my mom for encouraging me to pursue a career in medicine when I could have been safe as a professor in a lab and classroom. Angry at myself for the carelessness that led to my needlestick injury. And angry at a system that put inexperienced doctors like me on the frontlines where we could harm ourselves. I wanted to quit. I was supposed to be working in service of others, but all I seemed to be able to do was feel sorry for myself. I did not have an ounce of energy left to give to anyone.

As my vacation came to an end, I didn't want to return to residency. The needlestick injury was my breaking point in what had been several demoralizing months. My enthusiasm was quickly eclipsed by misery from constantly facing suffering and death, always feeling unprepared and inadequate, and never having time to catch my breath–let alone time to properly eat, sleep, or exercise–during eighty-hour work weeks.

Somehow, I boarded the flight heading back to San Francisco. The hills and small houses that used to seem pretty now looked threatening. The highway sign with the white letters spelling out the city's name that had welcomed me months earlier made me nauseous. I associated San Francisco with being an intern, and associated being an intern with feeling incompetent, overworked, and a needlestick injury.

I went numb. In the mornings, I would lay in bed, staring at the ceiling trying to motivate myself to go to work. I tried to do my work as quickly as possible and get out of the hospital. I felt like a ghost of my former self. But I saw no other way to protect myself. Even the relieving news that I had not contracted HIV or hepatitis C from my sloppy mistake barely registered.

I went through the motions of being a doctor, but I had lost my joy for medicine. I remembered how bad the beginning of medical school was and how badly I wanted to quit. Would things get better or was this just life in medicine? I didn't know.

8

Ms. Jones was gasping for air despite a mask pushing oxygen into her nose and mouth.

She was 76 years old. An aggressive breast cancer had spread throughout her body, including her lungs.

"Ms. Jones, when did you start having trouble with your breathing?" I asked, resting my hand on the back of her hand.

She was sitting upright in the hospital bed and I was sitting in a chair adjacent to her bed. Her husband was standing next to her, rubbing her back.

"I...have...cancer...everywhere. I...feel...like my...body...is failing," she said slowly as she struggled to breathe. I could see tears running down Mr. Jones's face as he moved his hands from Ms. Jones's back to tightly grip her left hand.

I thought of Mamanjoon, my 89-year-old grandmother, Aghajoon's wife. Earlier that month, she fell and broke her hip, and the surgery that followed was complicated by a severe infection. She had become frail even before her fall, and I called my family in Iran to strongly advise against heroic life saving measures like CPR because the likelihood of any meaningful recovery for Mamanjoon at the age of 89 with such a severe illness was next to nothing. CPR could save her life, but what state would she be left in and would she want to live that way?

Months before Mamanjoon became sick, I had performed CPR on an elderly patient who had a cardiac arrest. I felt her brittle ribs crack as I compressed her chest to try to jump start her heart. The patient died two days later in a coma. I did not want my Mamanjoon to face the same fate with medical providers cracking her ribs as her soul attempted to peacefully leave this world.

Unfortunately, Mamanjoon had a cardiac arrest caused by her severe infection. And unfortunately, she received CPR in Iran, as I had feared she would. The events left her comatose and connected to a breathing machine.

After three painful and distressing weeks, my family in Iran finally decided to disconnect the ventilator. Mamanjoon died moments later. I could not stop crying from the pain of knowing that my beautiful and loving Mamanjoon departed this world unconscious after weeks of being hooked up to machines. Aghajoon became deeply depressed, not just because he lost his soulmate after 72 years of marriage, but from having seen her suffer in this way.

Ms. Jones, like Mamanjoon, was nearing her end.

"Ms. Jones, last time I took care of you, you said you would want us to perform CPR if your heart stopped and do everything possible to keep you alive."

She nodded and looked at her husband.

"With your cancer continuing to spread, if things get worse and your heart stops, even if we perform CPR, I don't think you would recover from it," I said somberly. "So if this were to happen, I would not recommend we perform CPR."

She looked at me, then down, then slowly looked up at her husband. Then she looked back at me.

"No…I don't…I wouldn't…I wouldn't want CPR." She paused and took a few breaths. "Let…me…go…as soon as…I just…I just want to say…say goodbye…to my children."

We provided the oxygen she needed to stay alive and fluid through an IV since she was too breathless to drink.

After her children arrived and Ms. Jones said goodbye, she died peacefully a few hours later, surrounded by her loving family.

As I biked home, I found myself sobbing, my tears mixing with a cool mist of rain. The tears were for Ms. Jones. They were for the elderly woman who died after I cracked her ribs in a failed attempt to keep her alive. The tears were for my loving Mamanjoon who didn't get to say goodbye to anyone.

But they were also tears of joy. I helped a mother fulfill her final wish of saying goodbye to her children. I saw the impact I could have in medicine if I just kept going despite how hard it was. Reinvigorated, I shook off my despair and got back to work.

9

"**A** 62-year-old woman was found down in Golden Gate Park," my co-intern described to Dr. Harry Hollander, director of our internal medicine residency program at UCSF. "Her body temperature and blood pressure were both low."

"Tell me about her eyebrows," he nonchalantly requested.

"The eyebrows?!" I thought to myself, "We spent months of medical school on the heart, the kidneys, the lungs...but the eyebrows?!"

During my intern year, the hours were long, and the learning curve was steep. I took refuge in what had become my favorite hour of the day: morning report. It was where I learned from great teachers and nourished my passion for the beauty of diagnostic reasoning. And it reminded me of the session I'd observed with Dr. Dhaliwal on my interview day that crystallized my desire to train at UCSF.

My fellow residents and I whispered to each other: Why

would a patient have a low body temperature during the summertime? And why did Dr. Hollander ask about her eyebrows, of all things?

Dr. Hollander scratched his stubbled chin and adjusted his glasses. He explained that thinning of the lateral third of the eyebrows can be a clue to severe hypothyroidism. Indeed, the patient had thinning of her outer eyebrows. Bloodwork confirmed low blood thyroid levels.

Dr. Hollander became one of my greatest teachers. He seemed to know everything about everything. I wanted to learn how he became so knowledgeable so I could work toward becoming as expert as him one day.

"Dr. Hollander, how have you acquired such deep knowledge in every area of medicine?" I asked him once. "You even know so much neurology, which is a completely different specialty than internal medicine!"

"Reza, during the early days of the HIV epidemic, I once sent a patient of mine to a neurologist. That patient returned to my office crying. The patient said that he was judged by the neurologist for his HIV infection. I learned neurology so I didn't have to refer my patients to that clinic again."

Dr. Hollander's life centered around his patients. They were his motivation for learning everything he could to help them.

I wanted to be like Dr. Hollander. I was developing a passion for diagnostic reasoning. Morning report became a motivator and guiding light in my training. I saw the lessons taught there as an opportunity to learn everything I could to provide the best possible care to my patients. I made it my goal to learn more and get better each day. After a rough start, I was finally hitting my stride.

10

"I am so cold, doctor," Mr. Morteza said, pulling his blankets tightly around him.

He may have felt cold, but he was boiling with fever. His violent shivering set his salt-and-pepper ponytail in constant quivering motion, producing a continuous scratching sound as it moved against the freshly starched hospital sheets. As the intern on call, my job was to identify the cause of his fever.

Most often, fever is caused by an infection like pneumonia (lung infection) or cellulitis (skin infection). As I gently removed his blankets to examine him, I saw a small line of tubing emerging from his chest. The tube tunneled under his skin to reach the veins that drained into his heart. Mr. Morteza's doctors used this to perform dialysis since his kidneys had failed due to high blood pressure. This portal creates an opening for bacteria on the skin to enter the blood, which can cause a deadly infection. My hypothesis that Mr. Morteza had bacteria in his blood was confirmed when a lab technician smeared blood on a plate and saw spherical bacteria grouped in clusters resembling bunches of grapes. This bacterium, *Staphylococcus aureus*, lives freely on the skin, but its invasion into sterile blood is potentially lethal.

Even with the right antibiotic treatment, Mr. Morteza would still have a 20% chance of dying from this blood infection. And there was another reason the odds were not in his favor: I was an intern, a first-year doctor, with just a few months of experience. Yet I felt confident that the diagnosis was a catheter-associated bloodstream infection, and the plan seemed simple: remove the contaminated dialysis line, continue antibiotics, and re-insert a new line a few days after the blood was free of bacteria.

When I started as an intern, I was paranoid about every decision. Terrified of making a mistake, I triple checked everything, and then asked others to check it too. I felt like an imposter. Actually, I *was* an imposter–I had an MD and a white coat but that was about it. Still, by the sixth month of my intern year when I met Mr. Morteza, I had become confident enough to manage the basics. And indeed, with antibiotics and removal of the catheter, Mr. Morteza began to improve.

Without the catheter, Mr. Morteza could not receive dialysis. Without functioning kidneys or dialysis, his body would not be able to regulate his electrolytes, in particular potassium. Confident I was staying on top of things, every morning I checked his blood potassium level. On his second day without dialysis, I received a page from his nurse, "Mr. Morteza in room 12: potassium is 5.3." The normal upper limit for potassium is 5.2, so this was just slightly above normal. Still, I wanted to take every precaution to keep his potassium from getting high enough to cause him any problems. So, I ordered medications that reduce blood potassium by moving it into the body's cells and into the feces.

I left the hospital that day congratulating myself. I had not only diagnosed and treated Mr. Morteza's primary issue (the infection), but I had stayed one step ahead by monitoring for potential complications before they happened and treating them before they could cause him any trouble. *I'm starting to get this*, I thought to myself as I walked home. I smiled.

The next morning, I went to our workroom to receive updates from the overnight team. My freshly brewed coffee aroma mixed oddly with the smells of leftover half-eaten pizza and adrenaline-induced body odor from the residents who had been awake all night caring for patients.

I sat down amidst the multiple conversations between interns talking on the phone and with each other. As I scanned down my list of assigned patients and waited to talk to the overnight doctor, I noticed Mr. Morteza had been moved to the intensive care unit. My palms started sweating. Did I miss something? My face turned red. Did I make a mistake? My stomach spasmed. What happened to Mr. Morteza overnight that required intensive care?

"Your patient was found to be in a coma," my colleague

explained. "We checked his blood sugar, and it was almost zero, so he was sent to the ICU."

What happened to him? I wondered. Soon I realized what had gone wrong. I had made a mistake. One of the treatments I used to push potassium into cells was insulin. But insulin also moves glucose into cells. I had forgotten to tell the night-shift doctor to keep a close eye on his glucose, which fell to a dangerously low level and put him in a coma.

I had nearly killed him.

I wanted to take off my white coat, throw it in the trash with the greasy pizza boxes, walk out of the hospital, and never come back. I apologized to my colleague for my mistake. But she was not the one who needed my apology. *I'm not good enough*, I thought as I walked out into the hallway, fighting back tears. *I'll never be good enough.*

I handed my pager to my supervising resident and said I needed a moment to myself. I went to a call room, laid down on the bed and closed my eyes. My mind wandered aimlessly until I thought of Aghajoon. I needed his wisdom more than ever. I could picture him grabbing my hand and saying, "Reza jan, don't be so hard on yourself. We are all fallible as human beings. You will be imperfect in this imperfect world. The important thing is to learn from your mistakes to become less imperfect."

I owed it to Mr. Morteza and my future patients to understand what had happened. I had to reflect on what I did wrong so I could identify how to do better, to *be* better.

I went back to the ward and asked one of the faculty to help me understand where I went wrong. "Reza," she explained. "A potassium of 5.3 is just barely abnormal, and didn't require such aggressive treatment. He is recovering as his blood sugar comes back to normal, but check with me next time about your plan before you go home, OK?"

Having learned that I acted hastily from a lack of experience, I vowed to never make the same mistake again. But I had an even harder task. I needed to apologize to Mr. Morteza.

When I arrived in his room, I was relieved to see him looking much better than when we had first met.

"Hi Doctor," he said.

"I have to tell you something," I began nervously. "I made a mistake, and that's why you got sicker. I'm so glad you're better, but I'm so sorry. It was my fault."

"It's OK, son," he said. "I know you were just trying to help me."

I was humbled by the patient's compassion for me and for-giveness of my mistake. I was humbled by the practice of medicine—just as I thought I was hitting my stride I stum-bled and fell. And I was humbled by the lifelong journey ahead of me that would surely involve many more stumbles and falls, each an opportunity to learn, improve, and grow.

11

"Dr. Dhaliwal, I almost killed a patient."

His eyes locked with mine. He nodded, his concerned gaze encouraging me to continue.

I shared the mistake I had made that put Mr. Morteza into a coma. I was grateful the patient had been alright and accepted my apology, but I was still troubled by what had happened.

"Reza, thank you for sharing this with me," he began. "Mistakes are difficult to acknowledge, let alone share. I am proud of you for being so open."

Dr. Dhaliwal continued, "Once I was working a night shift as a junior faculty member, and I missed a heart attack. A patient had come in concerned about belly pain. I ordered some tests, including an EKG to make sure he wasn't having a heart attack, since rarely they can cause abdominal pain. The EKG looked OK to me. After I finished my shift, I went home, slept, and when I woke up, I reviewed the chart of the patients I had admitted overnight as I always did to recalibrate my decision making. I learned my patient indeed had a heart attack. Looking back at the EKG I saw that I had missed subtle abnormalities."

It was hard for me to imagine that my academic idol–the Michael Jordan of medicine–could make a mistake.

"Reza, we will never stop making mistakes. We are human. It is important to see mistakes as a chance to grow. It is hard in the moment not to feel defeated and blame yourself. But know that as long as you practice medicine with the goal of always improving for the next patient encounter, you will identify mistakes until you hang up your stethoscope."

I felt relieved. Dr. Dhaliwal had normalized making mistakes by sharing his own mistake.

Feeling more confident, I asked, "Dr. Dhaliwal, how did you become such an expert at diagnosis?"

He shared that he had started reading case studies in the *New England Journal of Medicine* (*NEJM*) as a third-year medical student. Each case presented a diagnostic dilemma analyzed by an expert clinician. He told me that by the time he had graduated from medical school, he had boxes and boxes of these diagnostic mysteries with notes scribbled all over them. He said, "They were my most prized possession, which I packaged carefully and shipped from Chicago to San Francisco when I moved for residency."

"I didn't just passively read these cases," he said, his eyes reflective as he remembered those early days in his learning. "I pretended I was the expert discussant. I didn't review the final answer until I tried to solve the case myself. I have not missed a single *NEJM* case record since medical school. I should clarify: I have missed many diagnoses while reading these cases, of course. But I have never missed an opportunity to learn from these cases each week."

I had thought Dr. Dhaliwal simply had innate talent. But it was his consistent practice habits that transformed him into a brilliant diagnostician. He was not naturally exceptional. I left his office inspired to grow my own diagnostic skills, hoping for a similar metamorphosis.

12

After my grueling intern year, my second year of residency was a huge relief. Work weeks went from 80 to 40 hours, with time to study–not to mention, cook, sleep, do laundry, and lift weights once in a while.

With my newfound time, I started emulating Dr. Dhaliwal's habits. I would visit the UCSF library on Parnassus Heights with its beautiful views of the Pacific Ocean and read clinical case reports for hours the way he had. Every hour I spent reading and learning, I developed more joy for medicine.

For each case, I pretended I was the clinician taking care of the patient. I would try to solve each case before the expert revealed their thoughts and final diagnosis. And these lessons translated on the wards. Not just with patients but in my new role as a second-year resident teaching interns.

I was not naturally gifted. I struggled to get into college. I struggled to get into medical school. During intern year, I wanted to quit. But I learned that anyone, regardless of their background can achieve expertise with specific, deliberate practice habits. The experts in medicine were not born that way. They were clinicians who had decided to dedicate themselves tirelessly to their craft. Over time, their tremendous and consistent hard work had led to expertise.

I was discovering that there were several elements that inspired my joy in medicine: scientific thinking as I learned from Dr. Stricker, compassionate care of patients as I learned from Dr. Holzinger, solving clinical cases like Dr. Dhaliwal, and teaching what I learned from each of them to other learners.

13

"Reza, my doctor son, can you help your Maman?" my mother asked during a visit to San Francisco. I was in my third year of residency training.

She explained that her left eyelid felt numb and tingly when she was stressed. And she had a lot of stress after her mother, Mamanjoon, died. Maman's life's purpose had been her children and they were now grown and gone.

"Mom, it only happens when you are stressed?"

"Sometimes I feel it when I am not stressed but it only bothers me when I am sad. I am concerned. What is wrong with me?"

"Don't worry Maman," I said. "I think it's just your stress. Maybe you could do some meditation or something." I gave her my final diagnosis. "It's all in your head, Maman."

My mom didn't believe me and went to her doctor. In fact, she went to several doctors. They all told her the same: just stress, nothing to worry about, all in your head.

It wasn't until five years later when she met a neurosurgeon at a dinner party and asked him if he had any idea what was wrong with her. He took his napkin, folded the edge, and touched her eye. She didn't blink as she should have. He asked her to come see him in his office.

He ordered an MRI that showed a brain tumor pressing on the nerve to her eye. Fortunately, the tumor was benign and wasn't cancer. Its growth was arrested by radiation therapy and her symptoms improved. But my guilt was incurable.

I had become accustomed to the sad reality of making mistakes in medicine. But a mistake in diagnosing my own mother? I felt terrible.

Fortunately, I have a very understanding mom with a wonderful sense of humor.

"Reza jan, don't worry," she comforted me when I apologized over and over. "In the end, I am OK. And remember, you weren't entirely wrong: you did say the problem was just in my head. And it was."

I was grateful for her forgiveness, but deeply troubled. Here I was near the finish line of my internal medicine residency, feeling sharp and confident after thousands of hours caring for patients and studying medicine over the previous seven years. And still I missed the diagnosis of a brain tumor in my own mother. I was about to start my first job as a teaching physician at Johns Hopkins Hospital. Was I really ready for this?

PART III

Impact

14

I only slept three hours the night before my first day as a teaching physician at Johns Hopkins Hospital. What if I made a mistake like the many I had made in residency, but now with nobody to catch it? What if someone asked a question and I didn't know the answer? I tossed and turned wondering if the patients, residents, and students would see me for the imposter I felt like.

I finally realized I had to be comfortable with three important words: I don't know. As a student and resident, I'd heard countless versions of the advice "Fake it 'til you make it." Appear confident and you will earn trust. Appear confident and you will get good evaluations. Appear confident and no one will challenge your decision-making. But I wondered, what is the point of appearing confident if you're not? I couldn't think of any way that would help my patients or students.

I thought of what Aghajoon might have said: "No one is expecting you to be a superb teacher or clinician on day one. You will be good but not great. You will grow your skills as a teaching physician, like you grew your skills in backgammon. But it will take time. And you will never be perfect. Reza jan, go to sleep."

This seemed like good advice, but what would it look like to own my uncertainty? I realized I would have to be comfortable saying, "I don't know."

15

Concerned by Mr. David's sudden confusion, his daughter called 911. At his local hospital, they thought Mr. David was having a stroke, but none was found on the MRI of his brain.

What they did find was that his liver had suddenly failed. But there was no obvious reason why, and so he was sent to Johns Hopkins Hospital, where I took care of him with my team of residents during my first month on the job.

"Did we check a Tylenol level?" I asked the residents. Tylenol overdose can cause liver failure.

"Yeah. It was negative."

"What about blood tests for hepatitis A, B, and C?" These viruses can cause liver failure too.

"All negative. Autoimmune tests too."

That was going to be my next guess.

I wracked my brain for other causes of liver failure. There must have been more. I tried to think back to cases I had seen as a resident, but I was frozen.

We didn't figure out the cause of Mr. David's liver failure. But just as mysteriously as he had become confused, he improved without any treatment. His liver tests spontaneously normalized. What was this mysterious illness that had attacked his liver and then left it alone? Although his liver had recovered, the resident taking care of Mr. David noticed a few of his toes had started turning dark and dusky. He now had tiny blood clots cutting off the circulation to his toes. His recovering liver had left a blood disorder called disseminated intravascular coagulation (DIC) in its wake.

What is the relationship between a liver problem that improved without treatment and a severe clotting disorder? I had just finished three years of grueling residency training, seeing thousands of patients under the guidance of some of the best diagnosticians in the country, and I still didn't know the answer. I wanted to be like Dr. Dhaliwal for my trainees. But I felt lost.

Rather than give up or guess a diagnosis, I tried out my new mantra with my residents. I confidently told them, "I don't know. I really don't know what's going on here. In fact, I have no idea. Somehow we need to connect the dots between reversible liver failure and blood clots."

"Well, I don't know about the reversible part," one resident said. "But couldn't the clotting disorder have occurred just because of the liver failure? Maybe the liver couldn't make anti-clotting factors while it was damaged."

"Of course," I replied, excited. "I was so focused on the mysterious reversal of his liver disease, and trying to find a common denominator for the second part of his illness that I forgot to think about an arrow connecting them directly. That makes sense, but we still don't know why his liver failed in the first place."

"Well, it must have been a transient insult that injured his liver," another resident said. "Or it wouldn't have just improved on its own. Maybe his blood pressure fell?"

"Great point," I said. "Low blood pressure can damage the liver, but it can recover if the blood pressure comes back to normal fast enough. But his blood pressure has been normal here."

"But maybe it dropped before he got here," a third resident on the team said.

"Excellent thought," I replied. "Let's get the records from the ambulance that transported him to his local hospital and see what happened on his way there."

Sure enough, the ambulance records showed that Mr. David had a significant drop in his blood pressure. It turned out he had an undiagnosed heart rhythm disorder that decreased the heart's pumping when it went into a dangerously fast rhythm. The heart problem caused the liver problem that caused the blood problem. We had an elegant solution for the root cause that explained everything, and fortunately, it was completely treatable.

Rather than 'faking it 'til I made it' by guessing a diagnosis or trying to hide my uncertainty, I openly embraced the mantra *I don't know*, and worked with my team to solve a case by thinking through things together and bouncing ideas off each other. I was reminded of what Aghajoon once told me. "Reza jan, no individual knows everything. But a group of minds together can know anything."

16

"Reza, Ms. Thomas is dead."

"Who's that?" I asked my resident over the phone. I was in line at the hospital cafeteria buying a morning coffee.

"Where are you?" the resident asked, sounding upset and anxious. "She was a new patient from last night. But she just died."

"On my way," I said, paying for my coffee.

Though I always let my residents present the full stories of their patients to me on rounds as if I'm hearing everything for the first time, I also read every detail of the overnight admissions early in the morning so I don't miss anything. And sometimes I peek in the patients' doors on the way to pick up my coffee just to get a sense of how they are doing.

So, in fact, I did know about Ms. Thomas. She was an 86-year-old woman with Alzheimer's dementia who had been admitted to the hospital with pneumonia. When I looked through her just barely open door, the hospital's fluorescent hallway light landed on an elderly woman who appeared to be sleeping deeply. I didn't want to disturb her. Was she dead when I had peeked in? I wasn't sure. I couldn't remember if her chest was rising with inhalation and falling with exhalation. Should I have entered her room and tried to wake her up?

Expected deaths in extremely sick patients are difficult enough to process but coming to terms with an unexpected patient death is even more challenging. From my own residency experiences, I could imagine the thoughts racing through the residents' minds: did we make a mistake that led to her death? Did we miss something? Should we just quit?

As I rode the elevator, I thought about how I could console them. I was not sure. There was that "I don't know" again. I decided to just listen and let them know I'd been through this too, as Dr. Dhaliwal had done with me.

I arrived at our team's workroom and sat down in a chair across from my team.

"I am so sorry about Ms. Thomas's death," I said.

"I just don't know what we did wrong," the senior resident responded with her head down.

"Why do you think you did something wrong?" I asked.

Surprised by my question, she looked at me, "Well she died, I mean...I just assumed..."

"Tell me about her case."

"We admitted her last night. She is 86 and has advanced dementia. She was not coherent, though she was very sweet and kept repeating 'Thank you' while I was examining her. She had a cough and fever, so I presumed she had pneumonia. And she did on her x-ray. So, I started antibiotics."

That all sounded very logical to me.

"But then I received a call from her nurse this morning that she had died," she continued, tearing up. "I feel so bad."

"Well, would you have done anything differently?" I asked.

"I guess not."

"She was 86 and quite ill," I said. "Sometimes pneumonia is what ends a patient's life at that age, especially with advanced dementia. It just happened to be in the hospital. I don't think anyone made a mistake."

"Thank you," she said, wiping her tears with a napkin. "I feel a little better."

"I know how you feel. You didn't do anything wrong. One time I did something wrong as a resident that nearly killed a patient of mine. Remind me to tell you about Mr. Morteza after rounds. Does the family know?"

"I called them and told them to come to the hospital," the resident said.

We had one more responsibility: to console a family who just lost their mother.

As we walked down the hall to her room, I remembered a poignant moment from Dr. Holzinger's clinic. He told a young patient she had terminal stomach cancer. She started crying. He put one hand gently on hers and said, "I will be here with you every step of the way." I remember trying to hide my own tears, overwhelmed not just by this patient's life being cut short, but by Dr. Holzinger's incredible empathy and compassion. It was my turn to channel my inner Dr. Holzinger and model that same empathy and compassion for my trainees.

In Ms. Thomas's room, her three sons and her daughter stood crying next to the bed in which their mother's frail form was covered by a white sheet. They looked up as we quietly approached. Trying to be Dr. Holzinger, I was about to speak. But the senior resident spoke first.

"I am so sorry for your loss," she said.

"Thank you, doctor," Ms. Thomas's daughter said. "She lived a good life. You took such great care of her," she said to my resident. "Thank you so much."

"Thank you, that means a lot," my resident replied.

I did not need to say anything or perform the role of the mentor I aspired to be. The resident handled it all beautifully. I had worked hard to become a teacher but realized that I was going to learn more in this job than the residents I was supposed to be teaching. We were all learning together.

17

"Welcome back Clinical Problem Solvers! It's Virtual Morning Report! Well, it's not morning here, but it must be morning somewhere in the world, right?"

I saw laughs among the muted checkerboard of participants in this online conference.

The yellow frame highlighted a young man in the top corner of the screen. "Hey everybody. My name is Rafa and I am a fifth-year medical student in Maringá, Brazil. I am so excited to present a case today!" He smiled broadly.

"Thank you for volunteering to present a case. Rabih and I are truly excited to discuss the case with you and the group," I said. "Who will be helping us scribe the details of the case on the virtual whiteboard as we go?"

"Hi, my name is Sukriti and I am scribing today."

"Thank you so much," Rabih replied. "Where are you joining from, Sukriti?"

"I'm a fifth-year medical student in Bangalore, India."

"Great!" I told her. "And who will be scribing the teaching points?"

"I am! My name is Andrea and I'm a seventh-year medical student in Lima, Peru."

"Thank you all so much for participating in Virtual Morning Report. Let's go ahead and get started," Rabih said. "Rafa, the floor is yours."

"This is a 42-year-old man who had loss of consciousness," Rafa said, as Sukriti typed the information on the virtual whiteboard.

"This is unbelievable!" I texted Rabih. "Virtual Morning Report is spanning 3 continents!"

"♥" Rabih responded.

"I can't believe just 2 years ago CPSolvers was just you and me podcasting from our basements!" I texted back.

"♥ ♥ ♥" Rabih replied.

Rabih and I were residents together at UCSF. We bonded over our common love of morning report. He often sat quietly in the back of the conference room. When he did speak, the clarity and logic of his stepwise approach to clinical problems was inspirational. I learned he was a math major in college, and so I nicknamed him "The Mathematician."

We quickly became best friends. We spent nights on call talking about medicine, teaching, and learning. We had both struggled with challenges in medical school and residency, and wanted to create a more nurturing space for our own learners where they wouldn't feel judged and wouldn't feel pressured to "Fake it 'til they make it." We wanted to foster an environment where saying *I don't know* would be seen as an expression of humility rather than as a deficiency in knowledge, where every *I don't know* could be seen as an opportunity to learn together.

While most of medical education focuses on transmission of knowledge, we wanted to focus on the process of learning how to *think* medically. We felt privileged to have learned this from Gurpreet's morning reports but wanted to share what we had learned beyond the walls of our institutions. So, we decided to launch a podcast–Clinical Problem Solvers (CPSolvers for short)–in which we would highlight the journey of going step-by-step from symptom to diagnosis. After we recorded our first episode in November 2018, we shared it with close friends and family. They thought the content was good, but that we sounded too robotic. They encouraged us to relax and just be our silly selves in order to create a casual and fun learning environment. We re-recorded the episode and released it. Within one month we were amazed to discover we had a few thousand subscribers and so we began releasing episodes every week.

Our podcast was rapidly gaining a following, and we loved getting feedback from our listeners on social media. But something was missing. When the COVID-19 pandemic struck and students were not able to attend medical school in person, we realized what we were missing and what the students were missing was the same thing: a real time, back-and-forth exchange between teachers and learners. In an attempt to fill this void, we launched live case discussions online as a series we called "Virtual Morning Report."

As Rafa continued to present his case from Brazil, Rabih must have noticed me silently shaking my head slowly.

"Reza jan, tearing up, brother?" Rabih texted.

"This is just so amazing," I texted back. "I never would have imagined! I am so grateful for you!"

"♥ ♥ ♥" Rabih summed it up.

Our listeners encouraged us to go beyond just teaching clinical reasoning and to use our platform to discuss racism and sexism in medicine. We expanded our team of experts and launched our *Anti-racism in Medicine* series and *Women in Diagnosis* series. Additionally, team members who joined us from all over the world began translating our teaching content into different languages to help us carry out our simple mission statement: to democratize the teaching of diagnostic reasoning. Although we created CPSolvers to teach, we have learned so much from everyone who has joined us in this work.

Rabih had indeed caught me tearing up. I was so moved to be a part of this amazing global community convening in the midst of a pandemic to share a passion for learning medicine. But I was also moved by the journey that had brought me to that moment. After barely getting into college, being rejected from medical school, and almost quitting during my intern year, I felt so fortunate to have discovered my purpose, my passion, my academic soulmate Rabih, and a way to learn from–and share what I have learned with–our global CPSolvers family.

I had found true joy in medicine.

18

I had just gotten home and fallen asleep after a night shift when my phone rang. I reached for the phone on the nightstand. It was Maman.

"Hi Maman," I answered groggily, confused as to whether it was day or night.

"Reza jan, are you home or in the hospital?"

"I just got home and fell asleep, Maman."

"Sorry to wake you but I have some sad news, Reza jan."

I could hear her sobbing. Alarmed, I sat up in bed.

"Maman, are you OK?"

"Reza jan, Aghajoon died."

"No…" I began crying. "Maman, no…It can't be…It can't be," I lay back down and dropped the phone next to me on the pillow.

Aghajoon had taken a shower and had begun preparing his favorite meal, *chelo kabab-e barg*. He had marinated perfectly cut, cubed pieces of filet mignon in chopped onion. As his saffron-infused rice cooked and a sweet, floral aroma took over the apartment, he bathed and then lay down to rest. He never woke up. It was a fitting end for this angel on earth to clean himself, prepare his favorite meal, and then depart this world as peacefully as he had lived in it. He was 92.

"Reza jan, are you there? Reza?"

"Yes, Maman. Sorry. I...I...I can't believe he's gone." The combination of post-night shift slumber and shocking news left me dazed.

"Reza jan, I know. He lived a long and happy life. I love you, my son. Get some rest. Call me when you wake up."

I stared at the ceiling as warm tears flowed from the corners of my eyes onto my pillow. My grandfather, my first teacher, my hero, and my guiding light was gone.

My mind drifted between awake, asleep, and dreaming, fond memories of Aghajoon arising and vanishing. One scene kept coming back to me. Aghajoon sitting on our sofa below the window in the living room, his thin legs crossed, a steaming Persian tea glass in one hand emitting a sweet aroma of cardamom, a small notebook in his lap. He sat for hours each morning, filling the sunlit pages in an ornate script with a small black pen.

After drifting off into deep sleep for the rest of the day, I woke up and knew what I needed to do. I got to the hospital early and went to the gift shop before my night shift. I bought a black pen and notebook and placed them carefully in the pocket of my white coat. When I got home, I sat at my desk and took out the notebook.

I remembered once asking Aghajoon what he wrote in his notebook. He told me it was his poetry and reflections about the world.

"Reza jan, I write poetry to make sense of life and to teach others the lessons I have learned," he explained, after carefully closing the book and turning to look at me with his wise, loving, hazel eyes. "I want them to learn from my hardships and to know that life is a beautiful struggle."

And so I started writing about my experiences in my new notebook: what I learned, how I learned it, how much I still have left to learn.

AFTERWORD

"Becoming is better than being."
— Carol Dweck, PhD

We don't learn from doing. We learn from reflection. Throughout *Finding Joy in Medicine*, Reza gave us a front row seat to his introspection and the lessons that he (and we) will carry forward. That emotional intelligence matters as much as intellectual intelligence ("work on your EQ and your IQ"). That students can teach their teachers. That connecting your effort to your purpose and striving to get better at your craft can be sources of deep fulfillment.

Sometimes we are too busy to learn in the moment during training or work. But scribing those instances–whether in a private journal or in a book like this–gives us a lifetime to ponder and learn from them eventually. With each high and low on his journey to becoming a physician, we learned alongside Reza, who openly shared his sorrows so that his readers may find joy.

People earn the trust of others through a delicate balance of credibility and vulnerability. Reza's biography at the end of this book establishes the former, but his stories throughout the book reveal the latter. Just like Aghajoon, Reza wrote honestly so others can learn from his experience and "know that life is a beautiful struggle."

My favorite line in the book is the last, where Reza reflected on "what I learned, how I learned it, and how much I have left to learn." It conveys a state of equilibrium, where he is fulfilled by what he has accomplished and yet driven by how far he has to go. It is a reminder to all of us that it is possible to be both a masterpiece and a work in progress at the same time.

—Gurpreet Dhaliwal, MD

NOTES

Foreword

Does your face light up: Morrison, Toni. "Does Your Face Light Up?" Oprah.com, Oprah.com, November 2, 2011. www.oprah.com/oprahs-lifeclass/does-your-face-light-up-video.

Chapter 5

To study the phenomena of disease without books is to sail an uncharted sea, while to study books without patients is not to go to sea at all: Osler, William. Address on the Dedication of the New Building. Boston Med Surg. J 1901; 144:60-61

Nearly a third of medical students suffer from depression and ten percent experience suicidal thoughts. Medical students are three times more likely to die by suicide than peers of the same age: Paturel, Amy. "Healing the Very Youngest Healers." AAMC, January 21, 2020. https://www.aamc.org/news-insights/healing-very-youngest-healers.

Chapter 6

To observe him at work is like watching Steven Spielberg tackle a script: Hafner, Katie. "For Second Opinion, Consult a Computer?" The New York Times. The New York Times, December 3, 2012. https://www.nytimes.com/2012/12/04/health/quest-to-eliminate-diagnostic-lapses.html.

ACKNOWLEDGEMENTS

I thank my loving partner, Elizabeth Nilsen, RN, for her support of this all-consuming effort. She has been a constant source of inspiration and joy over the past six years.

I appreciate Mr. Roozbeh Aliabadi, Navid Vosoughi, DMD, Maria Theodorou, MD, Saman Nematollahi, MD, Nicholas Zaorsky, MD, and Will Garneau, MD for reviewing the first draft of the book and providing feedback.

I cannot thank Elisabeth Askin, MD, Mr. Greg Garneau, and Ramzi Dudum, MD enough for reviewing multiple drafts and providing crucial feedback. Elisabeth advised me to integrate stories of Aghajoon throughout the book and to stay true to my authentic voice. Greg recommended I communicate my stories in a way that transcends cultural barriers. Ramzi kept pushing me to make my writing more accessible to readers without a clinical background.

I am indebted to Dereck Paul, MD, whose superb skills in writing, narrative construction, and editing, as well as countless hours of conversation and coaching transformed my initial stream of consciousness into an organized story.

I am thankful to my mentor, Gurpreet Dhaliwal, MD, who reviewed multiple drafts and provided counsel throughout this writing process. I thank my academic soulmate, Rabih Geha, MD, for his graciousness and support in allowing me to take a step back from *The Clinical Problem Solvers* while writing this book.

I am grateful to Dr. Aaron Berkowitz for his editorial assistance. He truly helped me develop and realize my vision in the writing of this book. Aaron is a brilliant writer, storyteller, and above all, an altruistic human being who finds joy in helping others achieve their goals. If you want to see his humanity, humility, and captivating writing in action, check out his book *One by One by One,* which tells the stories of his work caring for patients with brain tumors as the only neurologist in Haiti.

I am fortunate for the support of my wonderful parents, Ms. Shahnaz Amiraslani and Mahmoud Sedighi, PhD, my wise and loving sister, Tara Manesh, and my best friend and brother, Ali Manesh, DMD.

AUTHOR BIO

Photo: © Deon Griffin

Reza's passion is learning and teaching diagnostic reasoning with the goal of helping others find joy in their health care training and careers. With Rabih Geha, he co-founded Clinical Problem Solvers, whose mission is to democratize the teaching of diagnostic reasoning. The CPSolvers podcast has listeners in over 165 countries.

Reza was born in Tehran, Iran. His family immigrated to the United States when he was 2 years old. He grew up in a suburb outside of Pittsburgh, Pennsylvania.

He graduated from the University of Pittsburgh School of Medicine and completed internal medicine residency training at University of California San Francisco, where he received the Jeffrey Weingarten Award for exemplifying the personal and professional qualities of a UCSF physician. His first faculty position was at Johns Hopkins University where he was awarded the Osler Housestaff Faculty Teaching Award.

He enjoys bodybuilding, long sessions on the elliptical, walks on the Chicago Lakefront Trail, and eating at Chipotle. He is not sponsored by Chipotle, yet.